An assessment workbook for the BTEC Award in WorkSkills

WorkSkills Activator Level 2

Judith Ball

Eileen Cox

2

A PEARSON COMPANY

Pearson Education

Edinburgh Gate

Harlow

Essex

CM20 2JE

© Pearson Education 2008

ISBN: 978-1-84690-335-9

Printed in China EPC/03

Page make-up and illustrations by Redmoor Design, Tavistock, Devon

Acknowledgments

The publisher would like to thank the following for their kind permission to reproduce their photographs:

(Key: b-bottom; c-centre; l-left; r-right; t-top)

Cover images: iStockphoto: Christine Balderas cl (hammer), tr (doctor); bluestocking tc (calculator); Ronald Hudson cr (parking ticket); Sergey Kashkin br (food serving); Kuzma tc (hard hat); Luca Manieri cr (plants); Martin McElligott bc (baking); Vladislav Mitic cl (tailors dummies); Dusan Zidar tl (haircut); Krzysztof Zmij bl (microchip); Masterfile UK Ltd: David Muir b (painters easel)

All other images © Pearson Education

Picture Research by: Sally Cole

Every effort has been made to trace the copyright holders and we apologise in advance for any unintentional omissions. We would be pleased to insert the appropriate acknowledgement in any subsequent edition of this publication.

Contents

Introduction

Work experience is an important part of education for employability, which allows you to learn about the world of work in a 'real life' working situation. It is important that you not only have a good understanding of what is required of you to get into the labour market, but that you gain the skills you need to succeed in it. Work experience is therefore a vital element in your preparation for working life.

This workbook is designed to guide you through the evidence requirements for the BTEC Award in **Work**Skills (the full Award is three credits). The sections may also form part of a larger **Work**Skills qualification, such as the Certificate (13 credits) or Diploma (37 credits). The BTEC Award in **Work**Skills can form part of the Additional and Specialist Learning of the new 14–19 Diplomas, as a minimum of ten days' work experience will be compulsory for every learner.

Learning Outcomes LO state exactly what you should know, understand or be able to do as a result of completing the unit. **Assessment Criteria** P are statements that tell you what you must do to show that you have reached a certain standard. They are the basis on which judgement about your work is made.

The book is divided into sections:

How to obtain a work placement, interview skills and essential information

This offers tips on preparing for an interview for a work placement, should this be required, and information on how to obtain a work placement.

Three selected units from the framework

Section 1: Preparing for work placement (Unit 26)

Section 2: Investigating rights and responsibilities at work (Unit 20)

Section 3: Learning from work placement (Unit 27)

The sections will give you some helpful guidelines on what to do before, during and after your work placement, and include a variety of relevant activities for you to complete. As you take part in the activities and complete the pages in each section, you will be fulfilling the requirements for the award of a **Work**Skills nationally accredited qualification with Edexcel. By doing your best in this book, you will be well prepared to do your best when you attend your work placement.

Teacher/tutor assessment sheets, Visiting teacher/tutor report and Employer report

As you complete the sections, your teacher/tutor or work supervisor will complete these documents as evidence of your achievement of the assessment criteria. A witness statement template can be found in the Teacher Resource Disk.

Glossary

Words that have been printed in bold are included in the **glossary** at the back of the book. Whenever you are unsure of what a word means, look it up.

About the authors

Judith Ball is a lecturer in the Construction Faculty of a large Further Education college. She has a wide range of experience in the areas of BTEC, Basic and Key Skills, ESOL and of working with Modern Apprentices.

Eileen Cox is a Coordinator of the 14–19 Programme, working with secondary schools within a local education authority. Her previous work as a lecturer in a tertiary college involved a wide experience of teaching, developing programmes and assessing learners, including arranging and monitoring work experience placements across all vocational areas.

Acknowledgements

The publisher and authors gratefully recognise the ongoing contribution of the staff at Pearson Education and Edexcel.

How to obtain a work placement

If you already have your work placement, you can move straight to Section 1.

The way in which work experience is organised may differ from area to area, for example:

- Your school/college or Careers Officer may arrange your placement for you and help you to complete all the necessary paperwork. You will be involved in deciding what area of work that you would like to spend your placement in and what you hope to achieve during your time there. Make sure that you mention your choice early on when you are planning your placement to allow the school/college or Careers Officer time to set up links with a company that matches your needs.

- You may be encouraged to find your own placement under guidance from your teacher/tutor. As soon as you have decided what sort of company you are looking for, you can find details in a number of places, e.g. the local papers, business directories, yellow pages or a search engine using search phrases that include the location or postcode. You will then need to contact the company, in person, by telephone or letter. It is best to contact several companies so that you have a number of options open to you, as often the companies may take weeks to reply or even not reply at all because they are very busy. Remember to ask somebody to check that your letter is correct as you want to create a good impression.

- Your parents/guardians may be able to offer support in finding a placement as they may know someone to contact in the line of work that interests you.

- Trident from Edexcel provides a service that will fully prepare and support you during your work placement. Trident offers a range of learning opportunities which, together with interesting and relevant work experience, will enable you to achieve qualifications to prepare you for the job market. There is a choice of placements across a wide range of employers, and all the work placements undergo a health and safety assessment to make sure that you have a safe working environment. The Trident Diploma offer guarantees you ten days of work experience related to your Diploma course. This can be taken at any time throughout the course and Trident will also support learners who obtain their own placements.

- Trident Online is an online work experience selection tool. This interactive service from Edexcel provides you with a single point of enquiry as you plan, prepare and undertake work experience, keeping you safe, well informed and supported. The website is easy to use and can be accessed from any internet enabled PC, which means you can make selections and track progress outside school and the demands of the timetable.

Interview skills

Some employers may want to see you before your placement is confirmed, and some may even call you in for an interview. Don't be worried about the interview; it is usually quite informal and friendly, but you still need to be prepared. Remember that first impressions count!

The purpose of the interview is:

- so that the employer can meet you and make sure that you will be suitable for the work you will be doing
- so that you can meet the employer and make sure that you want to work there
- so that you know where you will be working and who you will be working with.

Presentation

Make sure you are dressed neatly and look appropriate for an interview. First impressions are always important. If you are not sure what to wear, ask your teacher/tutor for advice.

Arriving for your interview

First of all, find out how to get there and plan to arrive ten minutes early. When you get there, report to the reception area or the main office, tell them your name and the name of the person you have come to see.

Communication

Look at the person when you are talking, and try to answer questions in full; avoid just 'yes' or 'no' answers. Smile and be polite – it costs nothing and always gives a good impression.

Answering and asking questions

Before you go to the interview, think about the questions an employer might ask you and what questions you might want to ask them, for example:

- What kind of work will I be doing?
- What will I need to bring with me?

Prepare for questions such as:

- Why do you want to come and work here?
- What would you like to do when you leave school/college?

Try to give positive answers, not answers like, 'I don't know' or 'Because I was told to'.

> **Remember!**
> If this will be your first experience of work, don't worry or panic! Everybody has to do this for a first time, and employers who offer work experience placements will do their best to help you succeed.

Essential information

Please complete this before you start your work placement.

You and your school/college

Learner name: ....

Name of school/college: ....

School/college telephone number: ....

Email..

Title of course: ....

Name of teacher/tutor/supervisor: ....

Your placement organisation

Please complete this on Day One with your employer.

My placement is with:

Company/organisation: ....

Address: ....

....

Telephone number: ....

Email..

Name of main contact: ....

Area/department I will work in: ....

Dates of my placement: ....

Days I will work: ....

I will start at: .... and finish at: ....

Insert below either a sketch of your placement organisation or an image from one of the leaflets/websites you researched.

Section 1: Preparing for work placement

Learning outcomes

On completion of this section you should:

- **L01** Understand the company or organisation where you plan to do the work placement
- **L02** Understand information you need before starting work placement
- **L03** Understand what the company or organisation expects of you during the work placement
- **L04** Be able to set goals for the work placement, including skills development.

Overview

Work experience provides you with the opportunity to explore the workplace. It is designed to assist you in the **transition** from school/college to work, to develop a greater awareness of your abilities and interests and to make appropriate, well-informed and realistic career decisions.

Work placement experience is unique because it means: doing real work in a real organisation; finding out what you are good at; behaving in a safe and responsible way; collecting evidence to display your new skills; learning to work as part of a team.

This section will provide you with the opportunity to find out how to research and identify important information about your work placement, to identify the skills, qualities, behaviours and attitudes required at the placement, and to set goals relating to what you plan to achieve from attending the work placement.

The new **Work**Skills qualifications are available from September 2008. This section forms one credit (the full qualification is three credits) towards the new BTEC Award in **Work**Skills, or as part of a larger **Work**Skills qualification such as the Certificate or Diploma. The qualification can also form part of the Additional and Specialist Learning of the 14–19 Diplomas which includes at least ten days of compulsory work experience.

Key terms

The following key terms are printed in bold throughout the book and are included in the glossary. Whenever you are unsure of what any of the words mean, look them up in the back of the book.

accurate	enthusiastic	persevering	sole trader
adaptable	flexible	persistent	shows initiative
businesslike	global	personality	thoughtful
competent	glossary	positive attitude	transition
cooperative	independent	punctual	trustworthy
creative	jargon	recession	willing
devise	methodical	reliable	
economy	organised	self-confident	

Finding out about the company/organisation

Before you go on work placement, your teacher/tutor will help you do some research to find information about what the company/organisation providing the work experience does and where it is located.

There are many ways of finding out this information, such as:

- looking at company leaflets/brochures
- visiting the Careers Office
- talking to a learner who has previously been on work placement
- making contact with your employer
- using the Internet.

Before you start, look at the activity on page 11 and think about what you plan to do and the type of information you will need. You might have to look at different types of information before you find what you need or you might find the information quickly.

Use the table below to record your planning and finding the information you need.

Information I need	How to obtain the information	Information I found
Location of the company	Internet	http://www.............

Your teacher/tutor may be organising visiting speakers (such as employers, careers officers and learners who have previously attended work experience) to attend your class to help you with your research.

Make notes of any questions you would like to ask the speakers.

Questions I need to ask:
Notes:

Remember!

Ask the speaker to explain anything that you do not understand.

Workskills Activator Level 2 Section 1

Finding out about the work placement

Complete the table below.

Name of company/organisation:		
Address:		
What is the main business of the company/organisation? Explain it.		
What is the daily time schedule at the placement?	Start time:	
	Finish time:	
	Lunch time:	
	Other breaks:	
Is the organisation:	a charity or voluntary agency?	
	a **sole trader**?	
	a private company?	
	a public service organisation (e.g. government department)?	
	a company limited by guarantee (ltd)?	
	a public limited company (plc)?	
Who pays for the services the company provides?	customers	
	the government	
	other (please state)	
Who are its main customers?	the public	
	other branches/ regional offices/ subsidiaries of the organisation	
	other organisations	
How many people work for the company/organisation?		
Does the company/organisation have branches nationally?		
Does the company/organisation have branches internationally?		
Is the company/organisation located near to my home?		

Finding out about your role at the work placement

Finding out about your role at the work placement

Think about:

a) what you need to know about your role before going to your work placement, for example:

- In what department of the company/organisation will you be working?
- Will you be expected to go in on Saturdays? (Remember, not all jobs are Monday to Friday, for example, retail work or hairdressing.)
- Explain the tasks you will carry out in the work placement

b) how you are going to find the information you need.

Record the information you have found below.

....

....

....

....

....

....

....

....

....

....

....

....

....

....

....

....

....

....

....

....

....

Preparing to go

Prepare for your first day by thinking and planning ahead about the things you will need.

Travel

How will you get to work?

a) List as many forms of transport that you think you could use to travel to your placement.

....

....

....

b) How long will the journey take? ....

c) What time will you have to leave home? ....

d) What time will you get back home? ....

e) If you are using public transport, what will this cost? ....

f) What problems might occur with these arrangements and how would you deal with them?

....

....

....

Lunch

What will you do for lunch?

Highlight or place a tick beside your preference:

a) take a packed lunch ☐

a) take money to buy lunch at work ☐

b) take money to buy lunch outside. ☐

Money I will need per day: £...........................

This will be to cover travel, food and emergencies.

Personal appearance

What type of clothing will you be expected to wear at your placement?

....

....

....

Information

You will need to read these pages before you go to your placement.

What if ...

... I am ill?

On your first day, you will need to find out what the work placement **procedure** is for reporting absence. Make sure you know who to pass the message to, and when you expect to be back. You will also need to contact your school/college supervisor to let them know.

If I am ill, contact:

Work

Name: ....

Tel No.: ....

School/College

Name: ....

Tel No.: ....

... I have an accident?

All accidents must be reported in a workplace. If you need first aid even for a small accident (like a cut finger), go to a first aid post or person, then report your accident to the appropriate person. (You will be introduced to the company/organisation policies on your first day at placement.)

Remember!

Do not use lifts where a fire is suspected.

... there is a fire or other emergency requiring evacuation from the premises?

Make sure you are familiar with the evacuation procedures and know where the fire exits are, how to leave the building safely and where to assemble. It is important that you go to this place quickly so that everyone can be accounted for.

Health and safety on work placement

It is important that you follow health and safety rules during your work experience placement. Before the placement starts, you should be aware of your responsibility to work safely, so as not to put yourself or your **colleagues** at risk.

Your employer will tell you on your first day what these rules are, and what sort of work you will be allowed to do.

At all times on work experience, including travel time, you will be expected to:

- act sensibly and safely
- take responsibility for your own actions
- conform to health and safety rules
- respect the equality and different views of others.

Make sure that you have understood what these rules are.

Every employer will expect you to …

- act responsibly
- follow health and safety rules and instructions
- be tidy in your work
- not do anything to endanger yourself or others, e.g. through misuse of equipment or messing around
- use only equipment for which you have received training.

Every workplace must have …

- a first aid box
- an accident book
- an evacuation procedure
- a person responsible for health and safety
- a person responsible for first aid
- a safe working environment
- protective clothing and equipment where necessary.

First aid

Remember!
Every employer is different. Make sure you know the health and safety rules at *your* placement. Everyone has responsibility for health and safety.

I know I have to be responsible for my own safety and the safety of others, and I will act responsibly at all times. If I am unsure about any health and safety rule, I will ask my supervisor.

Signed: ....

Date:.................

Challenges

How do I deal with…

… a problem at the workplace?

Talk to your workplace supervisor if you are finding the work you are doing difficult, or you don't understand what is expected of you. Think carefully about what you want to say, and try to explain your feelings clearly. Your employer has offered to have you there and will want to help you succeed, so don't be afraid to ask.

If you feel the work you are being asked to do is not what was agreed in your job description, you need to ask why; talk to your workplace supervisor, or contact your school/college teacher/tutor who can arrange to visit you.

> If you ask for help and are patient when trying to understand certain concepts or tasks, you will benefit from good outcomes in your work. If you deal with problems in a calm and mature way, you will be listened to readily.

… a problem with **communication**?

Often, you may find that people who are used to doing a certain job use **jargon** whilst speaking to each other at work. These are specialist words associated with that job that other people may not understand. They will not do this on purpose to try to confuse you, though it might feel that way, so ask for any terms you don't understand to be explained. Make a note of them, so that you will remember them in future.

> Ask someone to speak slowly, if you don't understand because of a different accent.

> Always ask for instructions to be repeated or explained rather than trying to guess. This will help to ensure you are working safely.

Tip:

Contact your school or college teacher/ tutor who will help you deal with a problem appropriately, if you feel you cannot talk to your workplace supervisor about it.

… a problem with my **colleagues**?

Work experience is an opportunity to work with lots of different people of various backgrounds, ages and possibly ethnic origins. You may not like everyone, and they may not like you, but you will all be expected to work together.

Workskills Activator Level 2   Section 1

Workplace values

Over time, the types of jobs that people do change. This could be the result of new technology, demands for different services, and changes in lifestyle, **global** competition or **recession**/growth in the **economy**. You may find that you have to change your job several times during your working life and employers are therefore looking for people who can handle change and are **adaptable**. They need people with a good mix of personal skills, qualities, qualifications and practical skills.

When you start your period of work experience, there will be many things to learn. There will be new things to do, new people to meet and new rules to understand and follow. Some of these things may cause you some problems at first, but how you deal with these problems will depend on your personal skills and attitude.

Attitude means the way you feel about things – the way you feel about work, about yourself and about other people. When you feel good about things, you usually do good work. When you feel bad about things, you often do poor work.

Discussion activity

Answer the questions below and then discuss your views with your class.

• Why do you think employers care so much about a worker's attitude and ability to get along with others?

....

....

....

• What are the personal presentation skills you need for your placement?

....

....

....

• What might a person do to improve his or her personal qualities or attitude?

....

....

....

For this activity teachers/tutors can find a group discussion observation record sheet on page 50.

Personal skills and attitudes at work

The activities on the next few pages will give you a chance to assess your personal skills and attitudes. You could then consider how you can improve or develop them further at your work placement.

Exploring personal qualities and presentation activity

Part of your experience of the world of work is about getting to know yourself better and how you get on with other people at work. Listed below are the qualities that employers look for in an employee. Look up any of the words you don't know in a dictionary. Then write the meanings in the space provided.

When you have written all the meanings, choose three words from the list that describe you best. Write each word on the '**quality**' line on page 19 and then write what they say about you in the space provided.

Quality	Meaning
accurate	
adaptable	
competent	
cooperative	
enthusiastic	
flexible	
methodical	
persevering	
punctual	
reliable	
self-confident	
thoughtful	
tidy	
willing	

Describe yourself activity

Example: Quality: reliable

I have not been late or absent from school/college during the last term. I always hand my work in on time. I always turn up to babysit for my cousin every Friday at 7 p.m.

Quality: ....

....

Quality: ....

....

Quality: ....

....

Personal quality words activity

Match the meanings

Write the number of each word or pair of words in column A in the space in front of the correct definition in column B. If you're not sure what the words mean, then look them up in the **glossary** at the end of this section.

A		B
1. businesslike	7	does not give up easily
2. creative		dependable; reliable
3. enthusiastic		being prepared to make a good impression; being a clear thinker and speaker; being well organised and well dressed
4. independent		being happy and excited about something
5. shows initiative		being interested in trying to do new things without complaining or arguing; a person who seems to 'look on the bright side' of things most of the time
6. organised		willing to learn; self starter
7. persistent		the way a person expresses himself or herself in relation to others; the things you notice about a person that have nothing to do with how the person looks
8. personality		determined; committed
9. positive attitude		able to think of very original ideas for making or doing something
10. trustworthy		being comfortable working alone, without a lot of help or supervision

Workskills Activator Level 2 Section 1

Personal goals and targets

The ability to set targets and make plans is the first step in improving your own learning and performance in any context. If you don't have a plan outlining what you are aiming to achieve from your work experience, then you cannot know how well it worked and learn from the experience.

Think about your personal targets for work experience

What are you most looking forward to doing on your work placement?

....

....

....

....

Is there anything you are worried or nervous about?

....

....

....

....

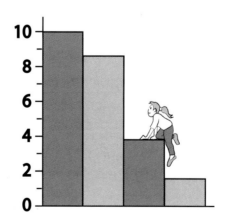

Personal targets activity

Set yourself some targets so that you know what you are trying to get out of your time on work experience.

Here are six examples. Can you think of any others you would like to add and why you think they are important?

My personal target	Why it is important
Go to work as agreed	It will create problems for other people if they are expecting me and I don't turn up.
Be on time	
Work safely	
Work carefully	
Show that I am keen about my work	
Get on well and work effectively with other people at work	

Before you go on work placement, your teacher/tutor will discuss your targets with you and help you to **devise** an action plan (page 22) so that you can identify what you are trying to get out of your time on work experience. This plan will then be reviewed with your teacher/tutor when you return to school/college, to help you reflect on what you have learnt from the placement and to identify any changes to your learning needs or career options.

My work experience action plan

Name of work placement:

My personal targets for work experience are:

I want to develop the following skills on my placement:

What evidence could I collect to show I have reached my targets?

Workskills Activator Level 2   Section 1

Reminder checklist

It would be useful for you to make a checklist to tick off on the day before you start your placement.

Can you think of anything else that you should add to the list below?

Have you:

- prepared your clothes for the morning?
- set your alarm clock to get up earlier?
- prepared your lunch?
- got change for your bus, tube or train fare?

> **Good luck!** Please be enthusiastic when you meet your supervisor – and work safely!

Learning outcomes

On completion of this section you should:

- **L01** Understand why rights and responsibilities are important in a workplace

- **L02** Understand why employees and employers have certain rights and responsibilities

- **L03** Be able to access sources of guidance and information about rights and responsibilities at work.

Overview

Everyone at work is protected by a series of basic legal rights, some old and some new. Changes are occurring all the time and people often have to seek detailed advice about their particular circumstances. It is essential, therefore, that you are aware of the importance of rules, responsibilities, workplace values, health and safety issues and working conditions before going on work experience.

Your first day at work placement can be a bit confusing. It is a good idea to know what will happen before you get started. This will enable you to achieve the best positive experience from the work placement.

This unit will provide you with the knowledge, understanding and skills you need to complete a process that prepares you for work experience. It will provide you with the opportunity to:

- understand why rights and responsibilities are important in a workplace

- understand why employees and employers have certain rights and responsibilities

- be able to find out how to research and identify important guidance and information about your rights and responsibilities at work.

The new **Work**Skills qualifications will be available from September 2008. This unit forms one credit (the full award is three credits) towards the new BTEC Award in **Work**Skills, or as part of a larger **Work**Skills qualification such as the Certificate or Diploma. The qualification can also form part of the Additional and Specialist Learning of the 14–19 Diplomas, as it includes a minimum of ten days compulsory work experience.

Key terms

The following key terms are printed in bold throughout the book and are included in the glossary. Wherever you are unsure of what any of the words mean, look them up in the glossary at the back of the book.

aggrieved	enforced	responsibilities	statutory
dispute	focuses	rights	tribunal
emerged	redress	scenario	

The importance of rights and responsibilities

The rights and responsibilities you have today come from a number of sources, for example, through Acts of Parliament and law made by judges, and some from European law. Together they form the British Constitution which is a set of rules specifying how a country is governed.

Unlike most other countries, such as India or the United States of America, the British Constitution is not written down in a single formal document. Instead, the rights and responsibilities we have as individuals and as a society are formed from a number of different sources. You will learn more about these sources as you work through this workbook.

Your rights and responsibilities

Activity 1

What do you understand by the terms 'rights' and 'responsibilities' as an individual – e.g. your rights and responsibilities at school/college, or as a customer in a shop etc? Make a few notes below.

> **Remember!**
> Refer to a dictionary or the glossary at the end of this workbook if you need help with this activity.

Rights:

....
....
....
....
....

Responsibilities:

....
....
....
....
....

How are these rights and responsibilities **enforced**?

....
....
....
....
....

When you go on work placement, you are technically an employee of the company/organisation. You do not have all the same rights as employed staff, but you have a number of rights and also responsibilities which you will need to be clear about before you go on *your* work placement to improve the quality of your experience.

> An *employer* is someone who pays others to work and is usually considered to be the owner of a business or the person in charge of a business.
>
> An *employee* is someone who works for another individual or a business, usually for wages or salary.

Rights

Everyone at work is protected by a series of basic legal rights that give everyone some protection. These rights are known as **statutory** rights. If a **dispute** arises in the workplace, either between employees or between employees and employers, it must be settled. Usually this is achieved at an early stage through discussion between colleagues or between the **aggrieved** person and his/her immediate superior. If, however, the grievance is not easily settled, then an official procedure is needed as all employees have a right to seek **redress** for grievances relating to their employment.

Responsibilities

Responsibilities are important and cover your general conduct within the workplace:

- time-keeping
- following rules
- wearing appropriate clothing, e.g. protective clothing, uniforms
- being clean and presentable
- behaving sensibly
- carrying out tasks you have been given.

List **two** responsibilities you may have at your work placement:

1. ....

2. ....

List **two** rights you may have at your work placement:

1. ....

2. ....

Rules

Rules are usually connected with specific work areas, equipment and activities. They are made by the employer to enable the rights and responsibilities of both the employer and the employee to be enforced.

> The *employer* has the responsibility to write the rules and the right to expect the *employee* to follow the rules.

Rules may tell you what you must do:

- Wash your hands before handling food.
- Always wear a hard hat in this area.

Or a rule may tell you something that you must not do:

- Do not use the lifts in the event of fire.
- All visitors must report to reception.

The main purpose for a rule is:

- It is a legal requirement, for example Health and Safety.
- It is to protect the public.
- It is to protect equipment from damage.

List three rules you may have to observe in your work placement:

1. ....
....

2. ....
....

3. ....
....

What are the reasons for these rules?

....
....
....
....

How are the rules enforced?

....
....
....
....

Rights and responsibilities at work

What could happen if these rules are not followed?

a) for the *employers*: (e.g. would their authority be weakened?)

....

....

....

....

....

b) for the *customers*: (e.g. they may be relying on receiving their order to meet their own deadlines)

....

....

....

....

....

c) for yourself or your *colleagues*: (e.g. would you or they receive an official warning?)

....

....

....

....

....

Workplace values

If you follow the rules and responsibilities, you will demonstrate workplace values. Can you identify a workplace value that you consider especially important?

....

....

....

....

....

Thinking about your rights and responsibilities when working with others before you go to your work placement will help you to be more confident.

My rights and responsibilities

Activity

People at work have responsibilities as well as rights. Some of these responsibilities are dealt with by law (e.g. health and safety) and others are not.

1. Working in pairs:

   • look at the tables of rights and responsibilities below and agree which of these is *always* or *usually* a **right** or **responsibility** whatever the circumstances.

   • decide which is *sometimes* or *never* a right on work experience and tick the correct box.

Rights

I have the right to:	Always	Usually	Sometimes	Never
1. ask questions when I don't understand something				
2. be heard when I want to say something				
3. decide what to do with my own time				
4. make mistakes without feeling guilty				
5. say 'no' to others' requests				
6. ask my supervisor to explain when they ask me to do things				
7. do the tasks listed in the job description of the placement				
8. refuse to do menial or repetitive jobs that last for more than two days				
9. be treated with respect				
10. ask to try things that will help me learn				

Responsibilities

I have the responsibility to:	Always	Usually	Sometimes	Never
1. arrive and leave on time				
2. listen carefully to health and safety rules				
3. look after my own health and safety at work				
4. be aware of the health and safety of my colleagues				
5. learn as much as I can during my placement				
6. follow my supervisor's instructions				
7. treat others with respect				
8. ask questions when I don't understand something				
9. work as hard as I can				
10. ask for help if I need it				

2. Compare and contrast your checklists with other pairs in your class.

As a class group, discuss:

- any disagreements including situations when you think the right or responsibility would not apply
- if there are any differences in rights and responsibilities between different types of workplace.

3. Agree a common list of rights and responsibilities which you can record and take with you to your work placement.

4. Discuss the need for responsibility and trust within the workplace.

> Your tutor will observe your group discussion as part of the assessment evidence for this element of your Award.

Information about rights and responsibilities in the workplace

Activity

1. Select **three** areas from the list below:

   a. health and safety
   b. equal opportunities/prevention of discrimination
   c. pay
   d. working time, breaks and leave entitlement
   e. contract of employment

From your selection above, identify what laws relate to them.

1. Identify **two** rights for each area selected.
2. Identify **two** responsibilities for each area selected.
3. Identify **two types of organisations/representative bodies** that employers and employees could access for advice on their rights and responsibilities at work.

Area 1: ………………………………………………………………………………..

Law relating to the area selected: ………………………………………………………

Employer rights related to the area selected:

- ………………………………………………………………………………………

………………………………………………………………………………………

- ………………………………………………………………………………………

………………………………………………………………………………………

Employee rights related to the area selected: ………………………………………

- ………………………………………………………………………………………

………………………………………………………………………………………

- ………………………………………………………………………………………

………………………………………………………………………………………

Employer responsibilities related to the area selected:

- ………………………………………………………………………………………

………………………………………………………………………………………

- ………………………………………………………………………………………

………………………………………………………………………………………

Employee responsibilities related to the area selected:

- ………………………………………………………………………………………

………………………………………………………………………………………

- ………………………………………………………………………………………

………………………………………………………………………………………

Information about rights and responsibilities in the workplace

Area 2: ....

Law relating to the area selected: ....

Employer rights related to the area selected:

- ....

   ....

- ....

   ....

Employee rights related to the area selected: ....

- ....

   ....

- ....

   ....

Employer responsibilities related to the area selected:

- ....

   ....

- ....

   ....

Employee responsibilities related to the area selected:

- ....

   ....

- ....

   ....

Area 3: ....

Law relating to the area selected: ....

Employer rights related to the area selected:

• ....
....

• ....
....

Employee rights related to the area selected:

....

• ....
....

• ....
....

Employer responsibilities related to the area selected:

• ....
....

• ....
....

Employee responsibilities related to the area selected:

• ....
....

• ....
....

List two key representative bodies that employers and employees could contact for advice on their rights and responsibilities at work:

• ....

• ....

Describe the type of advice that could be given to employers and employees from the representative bodies identified above:

....
....
....
....
....

Finding information about rights and responsibilities at work

You will need to do some research to find information on laws and key responsibilities at work for employers and employees.

You should use a variety of ways to find out this information, for example:

- looking at posters or leaflets
- visiting the library
- speaking to a member of a trade union
- using the Internet to visit a selection of websites
- guest speakers who may be invited to your class.

Before you start, think about what you plan to do and the type of information you will need to complete the activity on page 10 of this workbook. You might have to look at different types of information before you find what you need or you might find the information fairly quickly.

> Use the table below to record your planning and finding the information you need. You may undertake your research in groups and share the information you find.

Information I need	Where to find the information	What information I found
Information on the role of trade unions	Library; website	I spoke to my uncle who is a member of a trade union. He explained what trade unions do and what help and advice members can get for any problem at work.

Section 3: Learning from work placement

Learning outcomes:

On completion of this unit you should:

L01 Be able to present evidence of learning gained from tasks undertaken during your work placement

L02 Understand what skills you used or gained during the work placement

L03 Understand aspects of the work placement that could have been improved

L04 Be able to use learning from the work placement to set career-related goals

Overview

After completing a work placement, it is important that you **reflect** on your experiences as it enables you to build on the new skills you have learnt during your time with an employer. You will have been encouraged to keep a record of activities at your placement and this will help you in the review process.

On your return from work placement, you will have a **debriefing** session with your teacher/tutor. This session will enable you to discuss your strengths and weaknesses, what you have learned and the possible options for your future career.

This unit will provide you with the knowledge, understanding and skills you need to complete a review process of your work experience.

The new **Work**Skills qualifications will be available from September 2008. This unit forms one credit (the full qualification is more) towards the new BTEC Award in **Work**Skills, or as part of a larger **Work**Skills qualification such as the Certificate or Diploma. The qualification can also form part of the Additional and Specialist Learning of the 14–19 Diplomas, which includes a minimum of ten days' compulsory work experience.

Key terms

The following key terms are printed in bold throughout the book and are included in the glossary. Whenever you are unsure of what any of the words mean, look them up in the back of the book.

CBI	**evaluation**	**realistic**	**relevant knowledge**
debriefing	**expectations**	**reflect**	**transition**

Overall evaluation of your placement

Your work placement will have been a new experience for you. Fill in the following questionnaire which gives an overall view or **evaluation** of your placement.

Name:	
Placement company/organisation:	
Whilst on your placement, did you:	
• have a tour of your place of work?	YES/NO
• work on the same job all the time?	YES/NO
• work on jobs in different areas/departments?	YES/NO
During your placement, did you find out about any of the following? (tick as appropriate)	
• the qualifications needed to get a job with the company/organisation	
• the pay and future employment with the company/organisation	
• the training opportunities offered by the company/organisation	
• health and safety at work	
• job vacancies with the company/organisation	
Did you have any problems in the first day or two?	YES/NO
If YES, what were they?	

Before you went on placement, you may have had either a discussion with your teacher/tutor or a group discussion to talk about the different types of evidence that you would need to produce to complete this unit.

The evidence may include:
- a diary
- descriptions of tasks/activities carried out
- employer/teacher/tutor reports.

Gathering evidence from your work placement

During your placement, you will have carried out a number of tasks or taken part in activities that formed part of your job role.

List the tasks/activities that you carried out or took part in during your placement and provide evidence of the actual task or a signed witness statement from your supervisor or line manager. For example:

- I served customers and had to make sure I gave them the right change.

- ....

- ....

- ....

- ....

- ....

Whilst carrying out your tasks during your placement, you should have acquired new practical skills and/or knowledge. Complete the table below using the previous list and describe what skill/knowledge you learnt from each task.

Task/activity	New skill/knowledge acquired
Handling customers' money	I became much quicker at counting out different amounts of money.

Remember!

If you are not sure of what to include as a practical skill, discuss it with your teacher/tutor.

Employability skills needed to be successful at work

Employers expect young people to have the right 'employability' skills and these skills should be transferable between jobs.

The **CBI** has published a list of seven skills that it feels all young people should have when they start work. They are:

* self-management

* team working

* problem solving

* communication – application of literacy

* business and customer awareness

* application of numeracy

* application of IT

Discuss the meaning of these skills and how they relate to your work placement with your teacher/tutor and/or your peers. After your discussion, briefly describe each skill in the spaces above.

Personal skills

Work placement enables you to further develop personal skills as well as practical ones.

Complete the boxes below to provide evidence of how you developed your personal skills.

Skill	How was it developed?
Telephone manner	One of my jobs was to answer the phone calls of customers. This helped me learn to talk to a wide cross-section of people about a variety of things.

Strengths and challenges

Before going on your work placement, you will have an idea of what your strengths in the workplace will be. You should also understand that you may find some aspects of the placement challenging. After your placement, take part in a one-to-one or small group discussion about your strengths and weaknesses.

Complete the table below and on the next page to identify how your strengths were used and what challenges were met.

Strength	How was it used?
Good time keeper	I made sure that I always left home early enough not to be late.

Tip:

Your employer report at the end of this unit may help you to list and describe your strengths and challenges.

Challenge	How was it met?
Learning to use the photocopier	I had never used a photocopier before and, at first, I always needed someone with me to tell me what to do. Then, I became more confident and by the end of the placement, I was able to photocopy booklets, back-to-back, and to reduce and enlarge originals without any help.

Workplace activity sheet

People work in a variety of places. Find the workplaces listed below. One workplace cannot be found in the grid. Which one is it?

O	F	F	B	B	C	H	E	M	I	S	T	S	U
L	O	W	A	R	E	H	O	U	S	E	L	H	N
G	E	L	A	C	K	I	M	T	K	G	A	A	I
A	E	I	I	S	T	N	E	R	E	I	T	I	T
C	A	F	S	B	N	O	A	H	A	L	I	R	N
C	F	Y	A	U	A	M	R	B	A	F	P	S	E
O	A	R	I	C	R	R	O	Y	E	L	S	A	G
U	Y	D	R	E	U	E	S	C	H	O	O	L	A
N	R	N	P	R	A	M	C	H	A	R	H	O	L
T	E	U	O	O	T	A	Y	E	X	I	T	N	E
A	S	A	R	C	S	L	U	G	N	S	G	E	V
N	R	L	T	B	E	N	E	H	C	T	I	K	A
T	U	L	I	B	R	A	R	Y	M	S	R	E	R
S	N	A	E	G	A	R	A	G	E	J	L	E	T

ACCOUNTANTS	GARAGE	LEISURE CENTRE
AIRPORT	GARDEN CENTRE	LIBRARY
BANK	GYM	NURSERY
BAR	HAIRSALON	OFFICE
CAFE	HOSPITAL	RESTAURANT
CHEMISTS	HOTEL	SCHOOL
FACTORY	KITCHEN	SUPERMARKET
FARM	LAB	TRAVEL AGENT
FLORIST	LAUNDRY	WAREHOUSE

Improving work placement outcomes

Now that you have completed your work placement, it is time to **reflect** on your overall experience.

Do you think that:

- the placement lived up to your **expectations**?
- your job role was to your liking?
- your 'employability skills' have improved?

There may have been aspects of your work placement that did not go too well, for example:

- travelling to and from the placement
- carrying out the tasks/activities required in your job role.

Fill in the table below giving details of any general improvements that would have helped you during your placement and explaining how the improvements could have been made.

> **Remember!**
> You must only write general comments and not personal comments about your placement. Other people will read your comments, so you must be polite.

It may help you if you refer back to what you wrote as evidence for LO1 on page 37.

What could have been improved?	How could it have been improved?
Travelling to and from my placement	It would have been better if I had asked for a placement nearer my home as the long travelling time made me very tired.
I found some of the tasks I was asked to do very difficult.	I should have asked my supervisor for more help, but I felt too nervous to do so.

Work placements and future careers

Work experience plays an essential role in the **transition** from school/college to work. It enables you to discover whether or not you would like to follow a certain career, and how to set goals for your future achievement.

Think about how your work placement may have affected your choice of a future career. Has it stayed the same or have you had new ideas?

Use the space below to explain how your work placement has helped you make a choice about your future career. Two brief examples have been given, but you should write a longer explanation.

- Before I went on work placement, I thought I would enjoy working as a carer. Now I know that I do not have the patience to look after people, and I have decided that I would rather work in the retail trade.

- I have always enjoyed making things out of wood. I really enjoyed my placement working with a carpenter and I know that this is what I want to do.

....

....

....

....

....

....

....

....

....

....

....

....

Tip:

You could describe the tasks/ activities that you did/did not enjoy more fully.

Setting realistic goals

Work experience helps you to make **realistic** decisions about your goals for the future. It has provided you with the opportunity to explore a workplace and this experience should now be drawn upon to assist you in the transition from school/college to work.

Using the **relevant knowledge** acquired during your work placement, set short term and long term goals for the future and explain how you hope to achieve them.

Goal	How to achieve it
Find out what qualifications I need	Use the internet/ask my teacher/tutor/ talk to someone already doing the job.
Work towards the qualifications	

Letter of thanks

When you have completed your placement, it would be polite to write a letter of thanks to the organisation or company. There are several different ways to lay out a letter and a lot of different things to say about your placement, but one example is shown below.

Your address here

Date

Name of contact at company/organisation

Company/organisation address

Dear (Name of contact at company)

Re: Work experience placement

Thank you for allowing me to do my work placement with your company/ organisation. I really enjoyed my time with you and found it very interesting. I now have a much better idea about working life and know which career I should like to follow.

I would particularly like to thank (name(s) of people) for all the help they gave me during my placement.

Yours sincerely

(Sign your name here)

(Print your name here)

Teacher/tutor assessment – Section 1

Learners will need to provide evidence that addresses all the learning outcomes and assessment criteria for this section. Possible options include completion of the workbook, or discussions with the assessor that demonstrate understanding of the evidence requirements.

> The following evidence is listed as in the **Work**skills specification.

Learner Name: ....

Evidence required	Evidence meets standard ✓	Assessor comments
LO1. Understand the company or organisation where they plan to do the work placement P1 Explain key information about the company or organisation providing the work placement and where this information was obtained		
LO2. Understand information they need before starting work placement P2 Explain the terms and conditions of the work placement P3 Explain the tasks they would need to perform as part of the work placement		
LO3. Understand what the company or organisation expects of the learner during the work placement P4 Explain why workplace values are important for success at the work placement P5 Describe personal presentation requirements appropriate to the placement P6 Explain how they could deal effectively with situations of emotional stress, difficulty or confusion during the work placement		
LO4. Be able to set goals for the work placement including skills development P7 Set specific, realistic goals for the work placement, including a goal that relates to skills development		

I confirm that every reasonable step has been taken to ensure that the work presented is that of the learner named and that it meets the standard for this section.

Assessor: .... Signature: .... Date: ....

Teacher/tutor assessment – Section 2

Learners will need to provide evidence that addresses all the learning outcomes and assessment criteria for this section. Possible options include completion of the workbook, or discussions with the assessor that demonstrate their understanding of the evidence requirements.

> The following evidence is listed as in the **Work**skills specification.

Learner Name: ....

Evidence required	Evidence meets standard ✓	Assessor comments
LO1. Understand why rights and responsibilities are important in a work place **P1** Explain reasons why rights and responsibilities are important in a workplace **P2** Understand how rights and responsibilities are established and enforced in a workplace		
LO2. Understand why employees and employers have certain rights and responsibilities **P3** Identify the rights and responsibilities an employee has at work **P4** Explain the implications of employee rights and responsibilities		
LO3. Be able to access sources of guidance and information about rights and responsibilities at work **P5** Identify key representative bodies for employers and employees who would be able to advise on rights and responsibilities **P6** Describe the type of advice given by key representative bodies		

I confirm that every reasonable step has been taken to ensure that the work presented is that of the learner named and that it meets the standard for this section.

Assessor: .... Signature: .... Date: ....

Teacher/tutor assessment – Section 3

Learners will need to provide evidence that addresses all the learning outcomes and assessment criteria for this section. Possible options include completion of the workbook, or discussions with the assessor that demonstrate their understanding of the evidence requirements.

> The following evidence is listed as in the **Work**skills specification.

Learner Name: ....

Evidence required	Evidence meets standard ✓	Assessor comments
LO1. Be able to present evidence of learning gained from tasks undertaken during the work placement **P1** Show evidence that explains the learning gained from tasks undertaken during the work placement		
LO2. Understand what skills were used or gained during the work placement **P2** Explain how they used their strengths or skills during the work placement and where they experienced challenges		
LO3. Understand aspects of the work placement that could have been improved **P3** Explain any aspect of the work placement experience that could have been improved and how it could have been improved		
LO4. Be able to use learning from the work placement to set career-related goals **P4** Describe how the work placement experience might assist them in making choices about a future career **P5** Set short term and long term goals which build on their learning from the work placement		

I confirm that every reasonable step has been taken to ensure that the work presented is that of the learner named and that it meets the standard for this section.

Assessor: .... Signature: .... Date: ....

Learner's name: ....

Date of discussion: ....

Size of group: ....

Subject of discussion: ....

Learner Name:		
Evidence required	**Evidence meets standard ✓**	**Assessor comments**
Make clear and relevant contributions in a way that suits both the purpose and the situation		
Listen and respond appropriately to others		
Help move the discussion forward		

I confirm that every reasonable step has been taken to ensure that the work presented is that of the learner named and that it meets the standard for this unit.

Assessor: .... Signature: .... Date: ....

Learner's Signature: .... Date: ....

Visiting teacher/tutor report

The teacher/tutor's visit is an essential part of the work experience programme. It helps to ensure the quality of the experience by giving support, security and encouragement to the learner. Please comment under each heading if required.

Teacher/tutor's name: .... Date of visit: ....

Learner's name: .... Class/form: ....

Company/organisation name: ....

Address:..

Contact name:............................. Telephone: ....

Learner performance during placement	YES	NO
Attended every day		
Was on time every day		
Showed interest and initiative		
Was confident and asked questions		
Was able to carry out tasks independently		
Could communicate with new people in new situations		
Could accept authority and instruction		

Programme structure	YES	NO
Planned in advance		
Planned on a daily basis		
Learner was well occupied		
Periods of inactivity		
Work matched job description		

Supervision	YES	NO
Constant task supervision		
Mainly worked without support		
Supported as required		
Health and safety instruction given		

Review of targets

Please comment on how the learner met the objectives set for this placement.

Objective	Comments

Visiting teacher/tutor's Signature: ………..………………… Date: ………………..

Workskills Activator Level 2 Visiting teacher/tutor report

Employer report

This report will be of importance for the learner's file. Please add the appropriate response in each section and comment under each heading if required.

Company/organisation: ....

Learner's name: ....

Name of placement supervisor: ....

Dates of placement: ....

Attendance (Please tick)	
Did not attend	
Poor, no satisfactory explanation	
Some explained absence	
Good attendance, 90% plus	
100% attendance	

Timekeeping	
Often arrived late	
Sometimes arrived late	
Usually on time	
Always on time	
Always early	

Appearance	
Very untidy	
Tidy, but inappropriately dressed	
Appropriately dressed	
Tidy, appropriate appearance	
Very smart, appropriate appearance	

Attitude to work	
Lacks interest, only minimal effort	
Some interest and some tasks completed	
Interested, tasks completed on time	
Well motivated, conscientious	
Always looking for more tasks	

Continues over page

Employer report

Reliability	Yes or No
Needs constant supervision	
Reliable with supervision	
Reliable with minimum supervision	
Reliable and keen to take responsibility	
Takes responsibility, uses initiative, accurate and flexible	

Relationships with staff	
Uncooperative and difficult	
Participates with difficulty	
Cooperates and shows respect	
Helpful, keen and pleasant	
Very willing and makes a positive contribution	

Relationships with clients/customers	
Unhelpful or difficult	
Participates with difficulty	
Helpful and shows respect	
Helpful, keen and pleasant	
Excellent feedback, willing and positive	

Comments

Please add any further comments about what the learner has done or achieved.

Supervisor's signature: .... Date: ....

Thank you for completing this form.

Glossary

The meanings given for the words in this glossary are defined in the way they are used in their relevant section. The words may have other meanings as well.

accurate: careful, without errors

adaptable: able to adjust to new conditions

aggrieved: having a cause for complaint

businesslike: being prepared to make a good impression; being well organised, well dressed

CBI: stands for Confederation of British Industry and is an organisation that represents all companies and trade, employer and commercial organisations

colleagues: people you work with

competent: capable, qualified

cooperative: able to work well with others

creative: able to think of very original ideas for making or doing something

devise: plan or invent by careful thought

dispute: argument, quarrel, disagreement

economy: the wealth and resources of a community

emerged: came to light (as result of an enquiry)

enforced: made to comply

enthusiastic: being happy or excited about something

evacuation: removal (of people) from a place of danger

evaluate: think about and then write down how useful your work placement was

expectations: something you hope for

flexible: adaptable

focuses: concentrates

global: worldwide

glossary: an alphabetical list of terms or words found in or relating to a specific subject or text

independent: being comfortable working alone, without a lot of help or supervision

job **role**: what you have to do on a daily basis during your placement

Glossary

methodical: acting with method or order

organised: determined, committed

persevering: continuing firmly despite obstacles

persistent: determined, does not give up easily

personality: the things you notice about a person that have nothing to do with how the person looks

positive attitude: thinking about things in a useful and helpful way

punctual: on time, neither early nor late

realistic: seeing things as they are, based on facts

recession: temporary decline in economic activity

redress: remedy (a wrong/grievance)

reflect: think back to the time you spent on placement

relevant knowledge: knowledge related to what you need to know

reliable: can depend on with confidence

responsibilities: duties

rights: what is due to you

scenario: an outline of an activity

self-confident: being sure of yourself

shows initiative: willing to learn, self-starter

sole trader: business owned by one person

statutory: required/legal

tasks: the things you actually do whilst on placement

thoughtful: considerate of others

transition: change from one situation to another

tribunal: board appointed to investigate and judge work problems

trustworthy: dependable, reliable

willing: ready to do something